All About Letters
Alphabet Matching

by
Marilynn G. Barr

Publisher: Roberta Suid
Copy Editor: Carol Whiteley
Cover Design: David Hale

Entire contents copyright © 2001 by Monday Morning Books, Inc.,
Box 1680, Palo Alto, California 94302
For a complete catalog, write to the address above.

Call our toll-free number: 1-800-255-6049
E-mail us at: MMBooks@aol.com
Visit our Web site:
http://www.mondaymorningbooks.com

ISBN 1-57612-137-2

Printed in the United States of America
9 8 7 6 5 4 3

Contents

Introduction

Reinforce alphabet skills with matching worksheets, and alphabet playing and matching cards.

Matching Worksheets
Provide crayons for children to complete the worksheets.

I Can Match the Alphabet Booklets
Make construction paper folders to store each child's completed worksheets. Then provide each child with a booklet cover (pages 5–6) to color, cut out, and paste to the front of his or her folder. Write each child's first initial and name on the cover. Cut off the tops of completed worksheets and staple the lower part inside folders to display at open house.

Alphabet Concentration
Show children how to play a game of Memory or Concentration with the alphabet cards on pages 27–52.

Alphabet Practice Centers
Alphabet Cereal Match for Two
You will need a large cereal box, construction paper, markers, felt, and oaktag copies of the alphabet cards on pages 27–52. Cover the cereal box with construction paper. Decorate the top portion of the box with a title and cereal shapes. Glue a panel of felt to each side of the box. Color, then glue felt to the back of the alphabet cards. Cut the cards apart and store each set in a separate resealable plastic bag. Show how two children can practice matching felt-backed alphabet cards to each side of the cereal box.

Alphabet Polka Dots (cover)
Decorate a shoe box with construction paper polka dots. Write Alphabet Polka Dots on the box top. Reproduce, color, and cut out the matching cards and dots (pages 53–64) on sturdy tagboard. Store the cards and dots in the shoe box. Assign small groups of children to work together. Have each child in the group choose a card. Then have children place the matching dots face up on the table. Encourage the group members to help each other match and place the correct dots on each of their cards.

I Can Match
the Alphabet

_____
Name

I Can Match the Alphabet

Name

I Can Match
A, B, and C

Name _____

Draw a line to the letter that matches each picture.

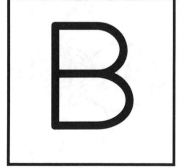
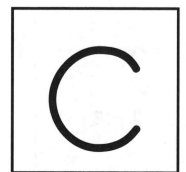

I Can Match
D, E, and F

Name _____

Draw a line to the letter that matches each picture.

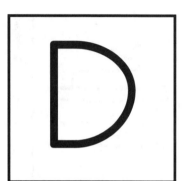

D

E

F

Alphabet Matching © 2001 Monday Morning Books, Inc.

I Can Match
G, H, and I

Name _____

Draw a line to the letter that matches each picture.

G

H

I

I Can Match
J, K, and L

Name _____

Draw a line to the letter that matches each picture.

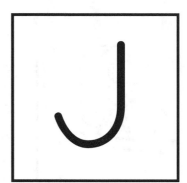
J

K

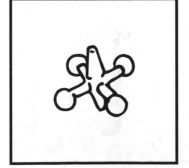

L

Alphabet Matching © 2001 Monday Morning Books, Inc.

Name _____

Draw a line to the letter that matches each picture.

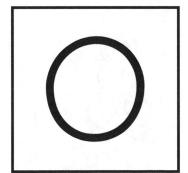

I Can Match
P, Q, and R

Name _____

Draw a line to the letter that matches each picture.

P

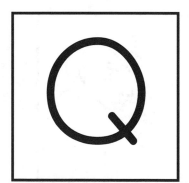

Q

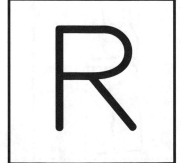

R

Alphabet Matching © 2001 Monday Morning Books, Inc.

I Can Match
S, T, and U

Name _____

Draw a line to the letter that matches each picture.

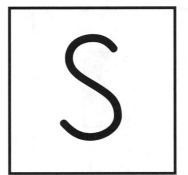
S

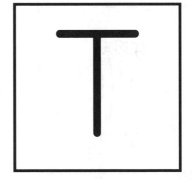
T

U

I Can Match
V, W, and X

Name _____

Draw a line to the letter that matches each picture.

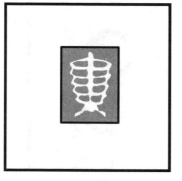 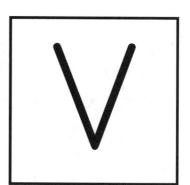

 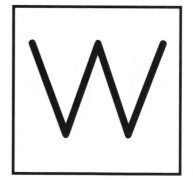

I Can Match
Y and Z

Name _____

Draw a line to the letter that matches each picture.

Y

Z

_____
Name

Can Match the Alphabet

Teacher

_____

I Can Match
a, b, and c

Name _____

Draw a line to the letter that matches each picture.

I Can Match
d, e, and f

Name _____

Draw a line to the letter that matches each picture.

d

e

f

I Can Match
g, h, and i

Name _____

Draw a line to the letter that matches each picture.

g

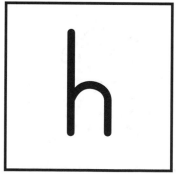

h

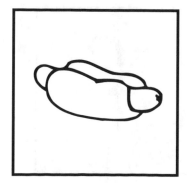

i

I Can Match
j, k, and l

Name _____

Draw a line to the letter that matches each picture.

   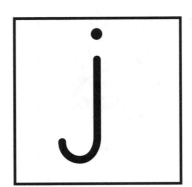
j

k

   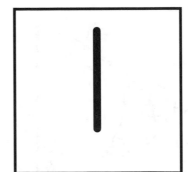
l

I Can Match
m, n, and o

Name _____

Draw a line to the letter that matches each picture.

m

n

o

I Can Match
p, q, and r

Name _____

Draw a line to the letter that matches each picture.

p

q

r

I Can Match
s, t, and u

Name _____

Draw a line to the letter that matches each picture.

s

t

Alphabet Matching © 2001 Monday Morning Books, Inc.

I Can Match
v, w, and x

Name _____

Draw a line to the letter that matches each picture.

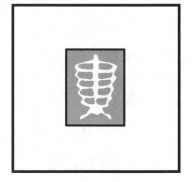

I Can Match
y and z

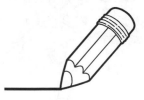

Name _____

Draw a line to the letter that matches each picture.

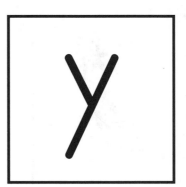

y

z

_____
Name

can match the alphabet.

Teacher

_____

Alphabet Matching © 2001 Monday Morning Books, Inc.

Alphabet
Matching Board

Alphabet
Matching Board

Alphabet Cards

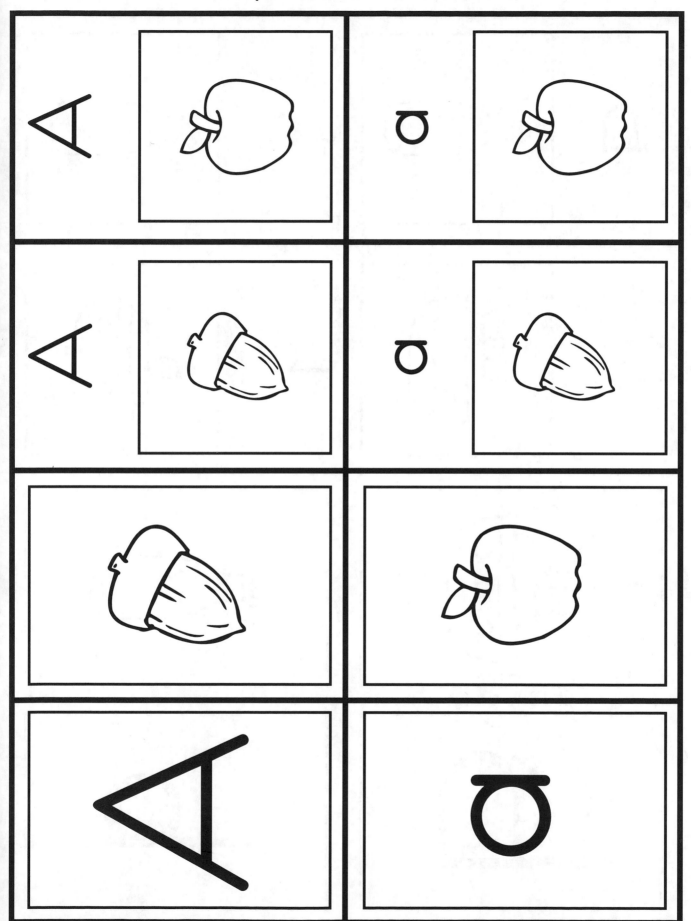

Alphabet Cards

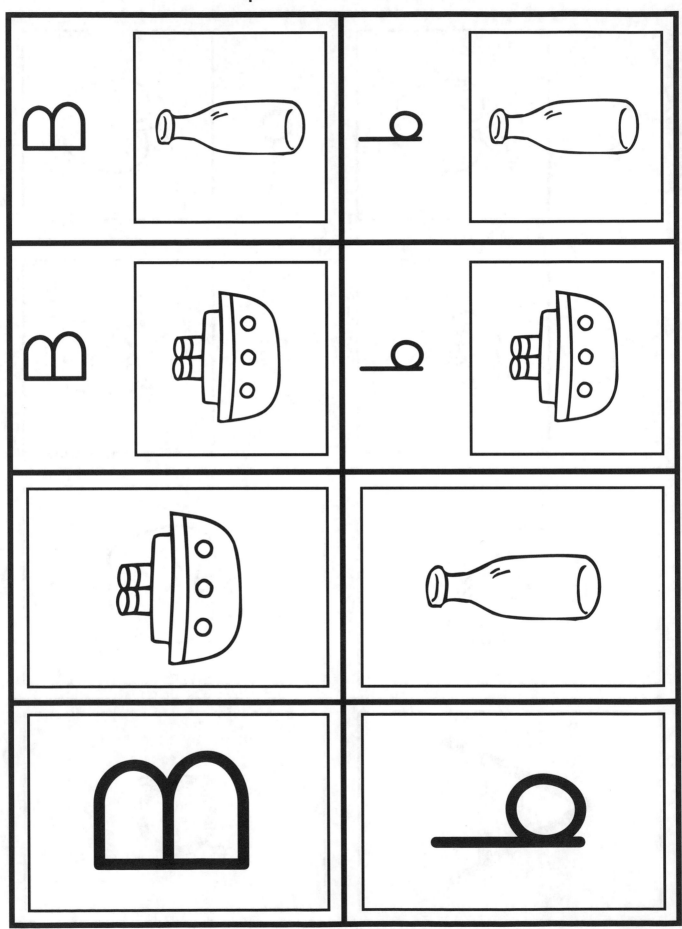

Alphabet Cards

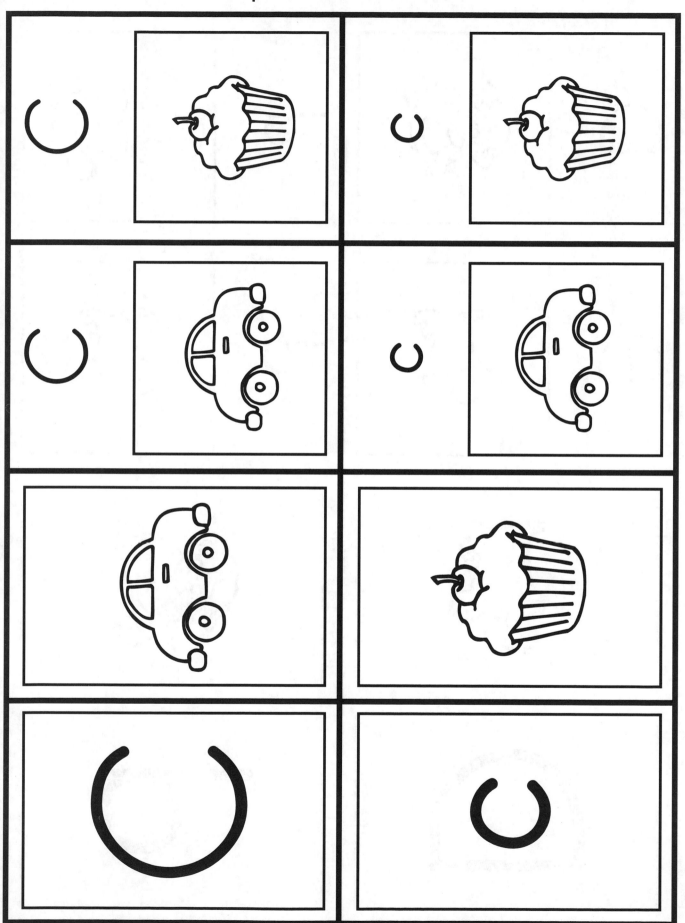

Alphabet Cards

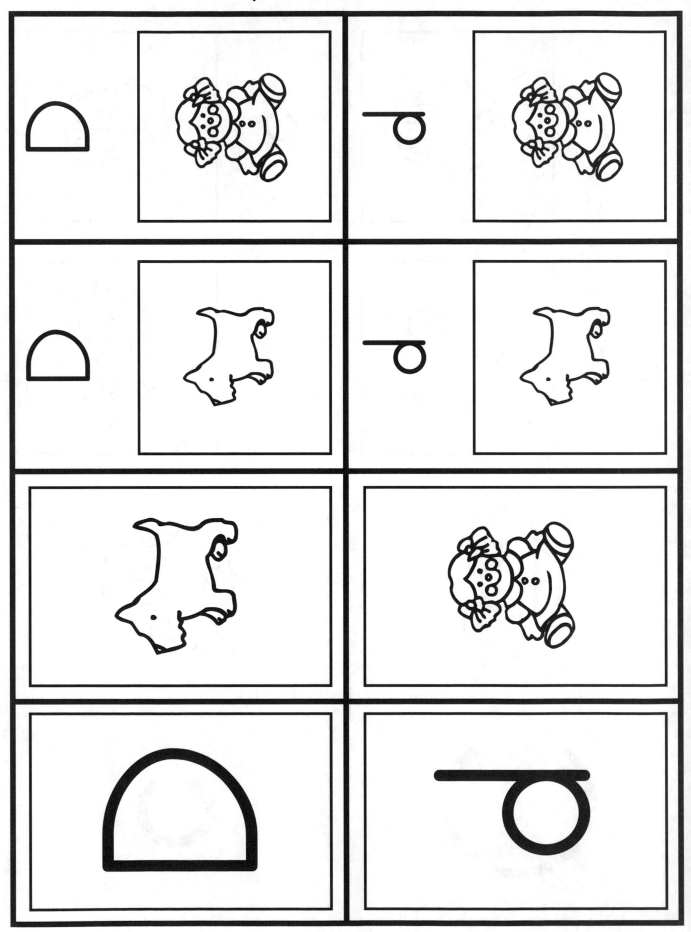

Alphabet Cards

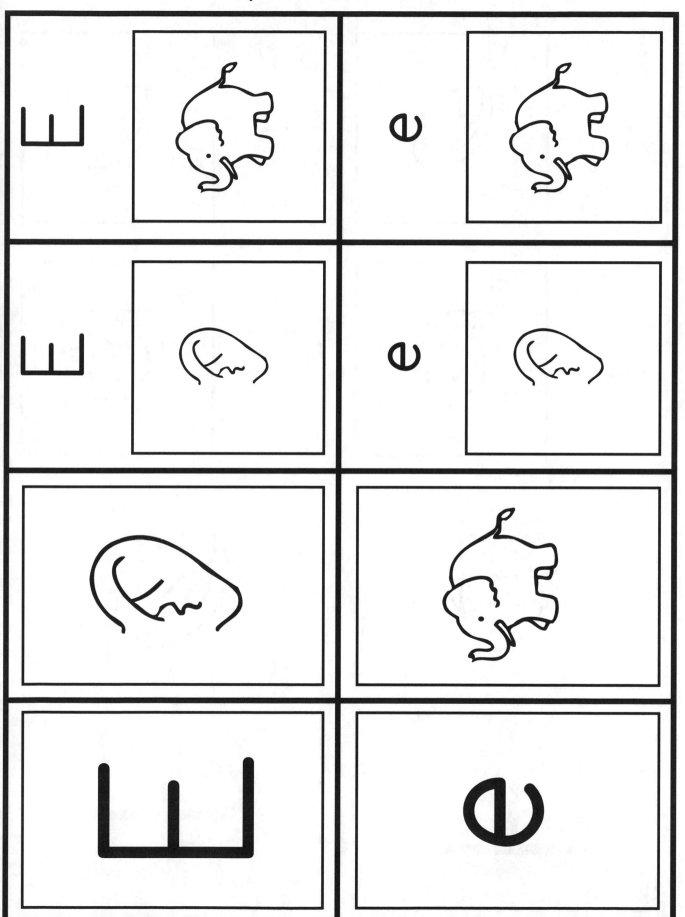

Alphabet Cards

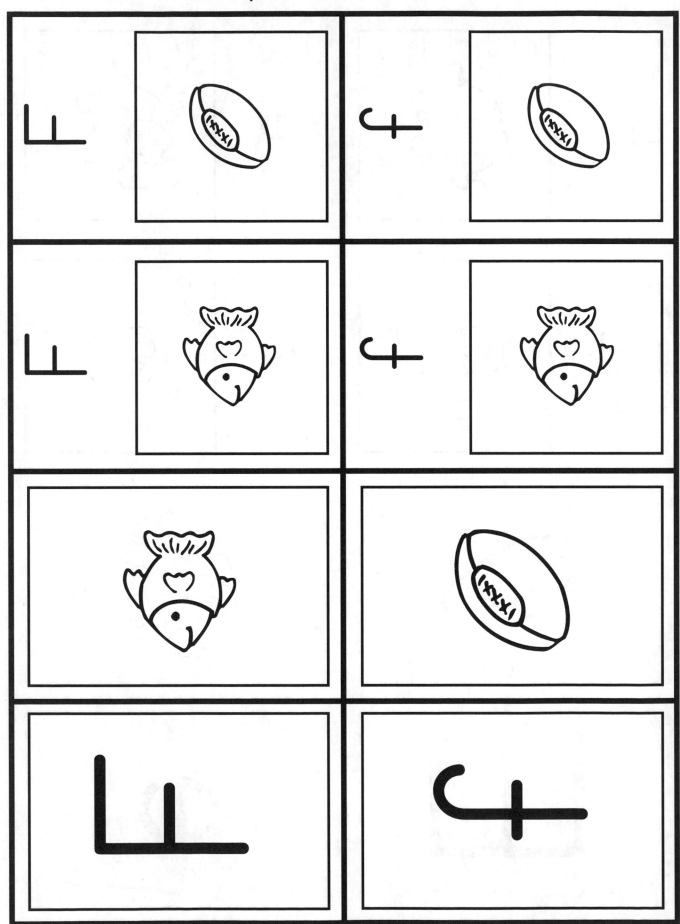

Alphabet Cards

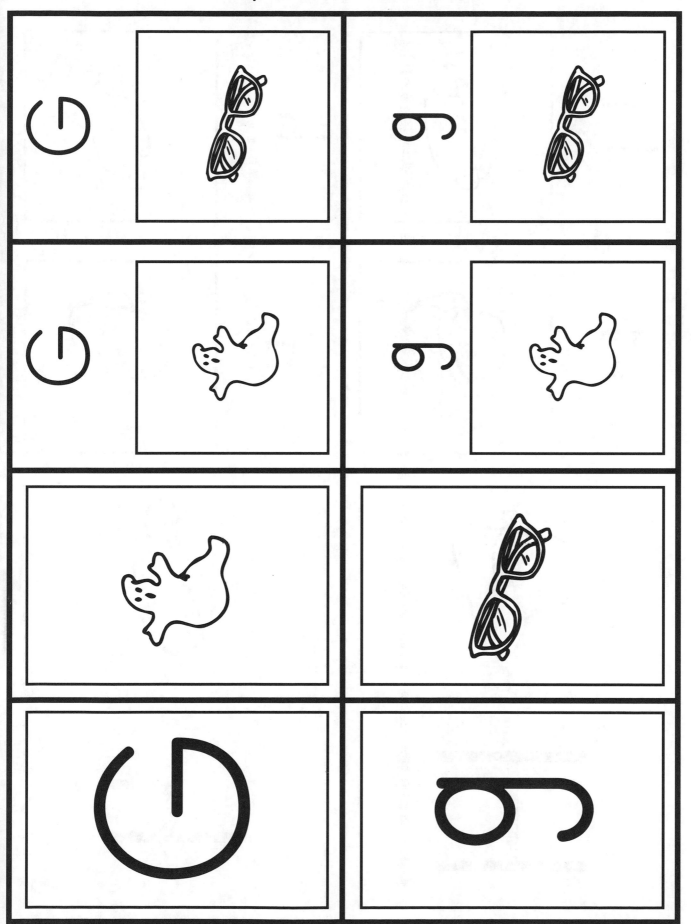

Alphabet Cards

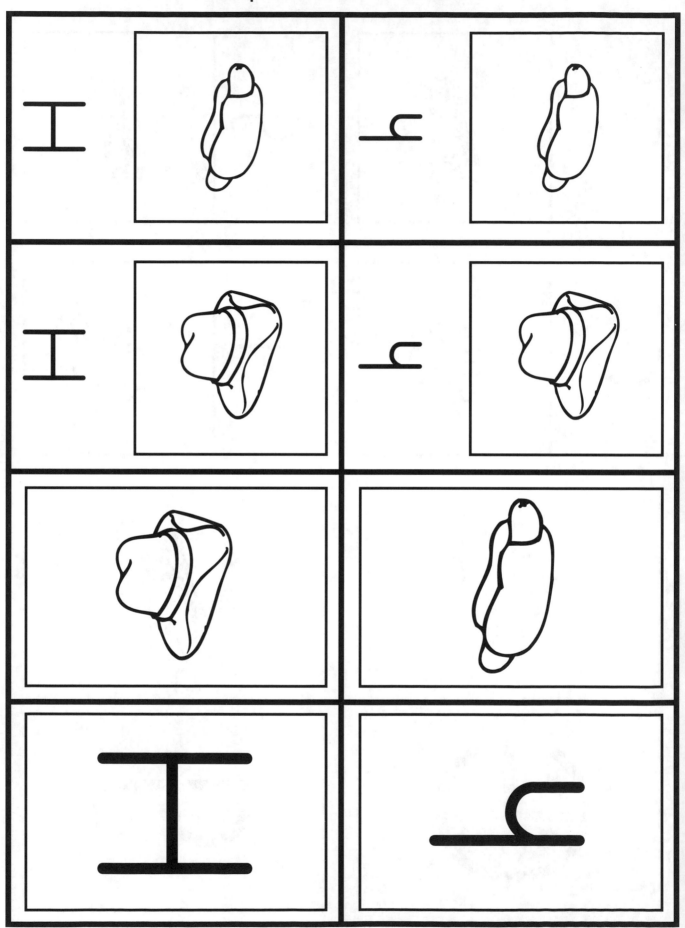

Alphabet Cards

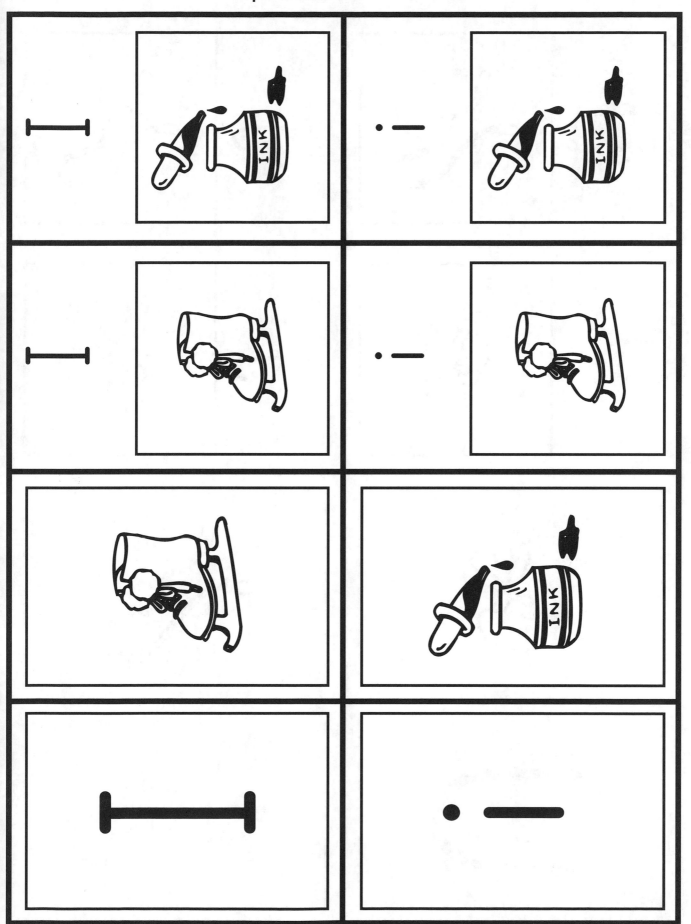

Alphabet Cards

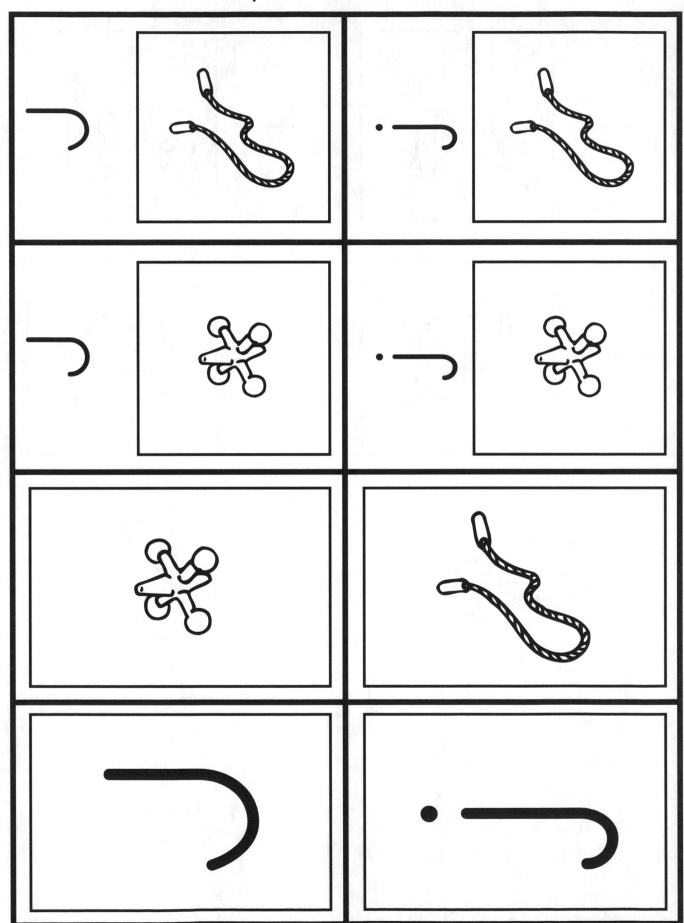

Alphabet Cards

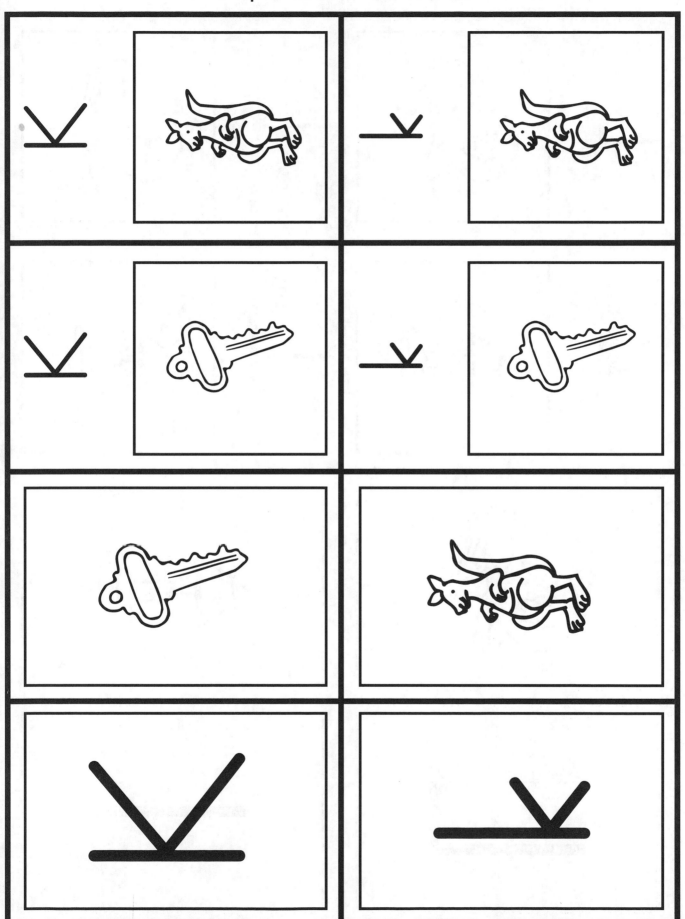

Alphabet Cards

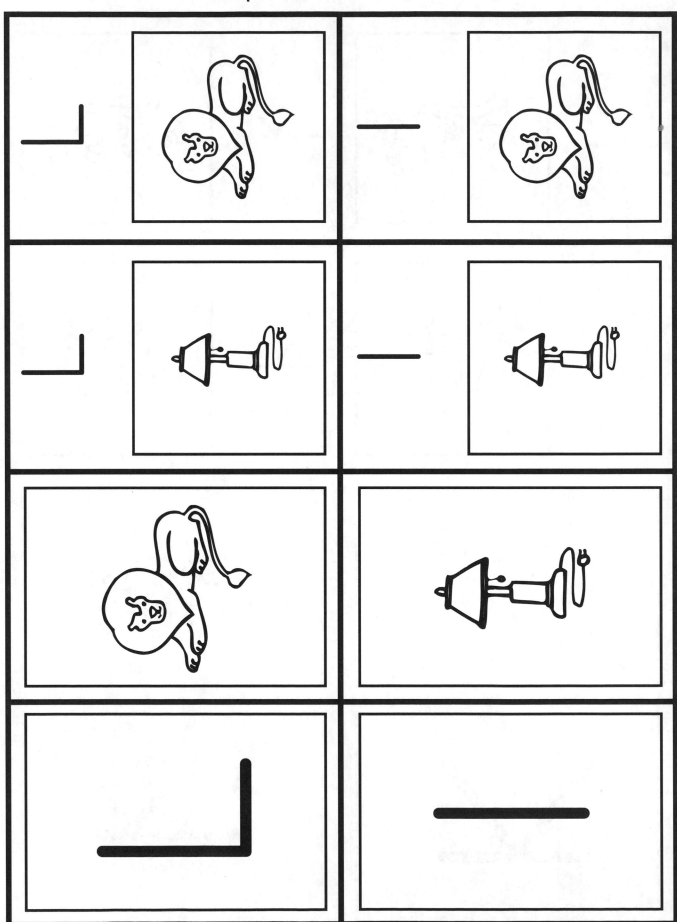

Alphabet Cards

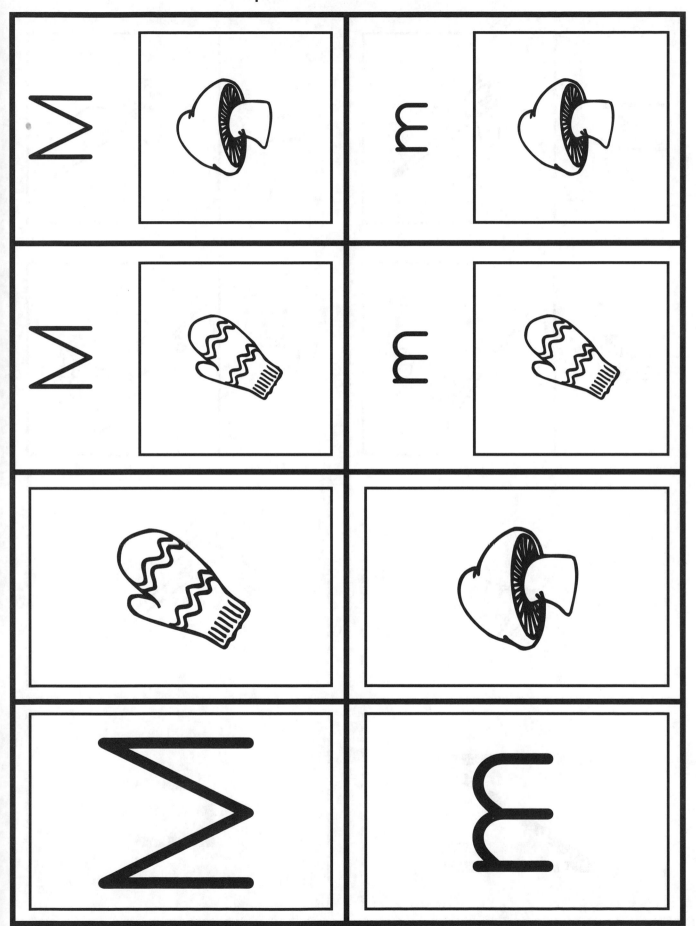

Alphabet Cards

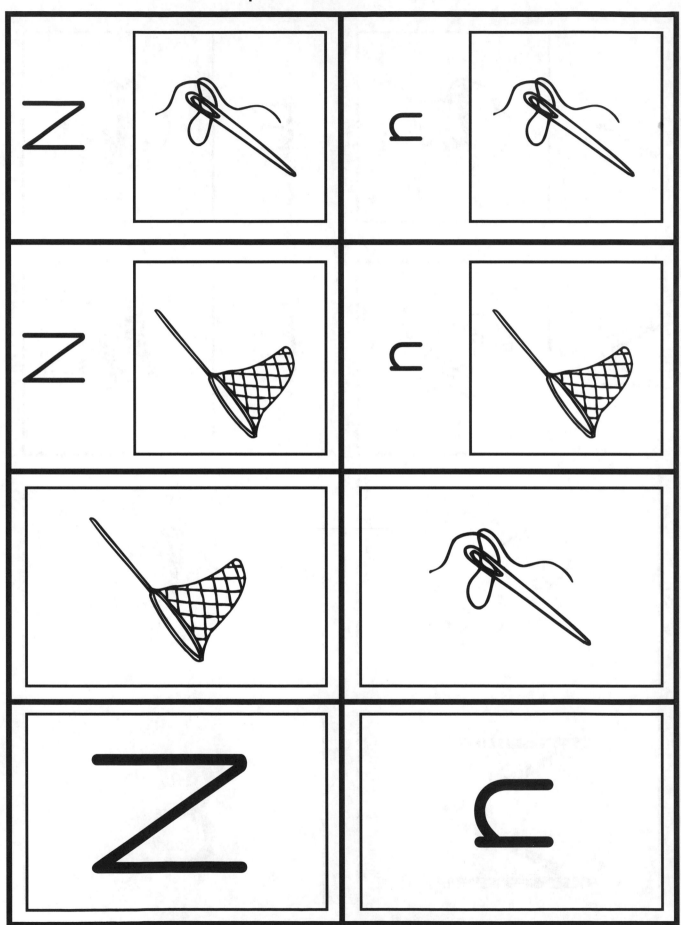

Alphabet Cards

Alphabet Cards

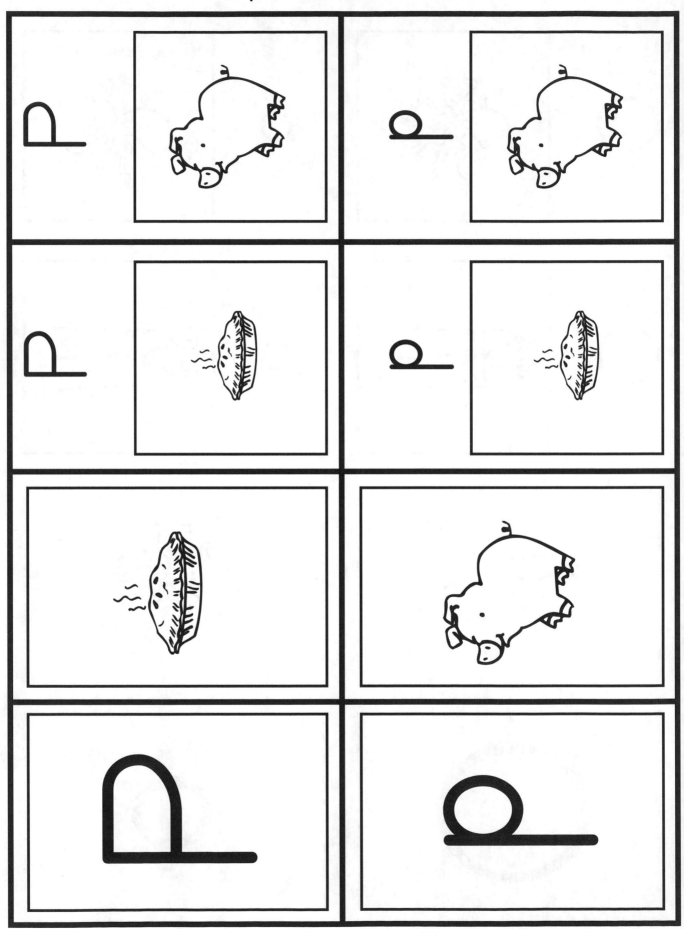

Alphabet Cards

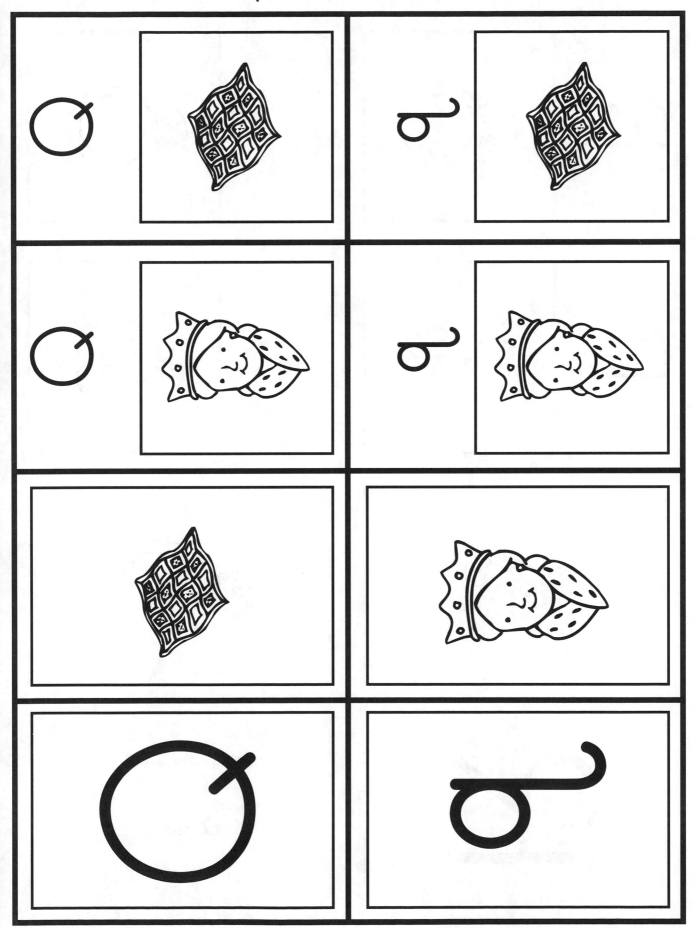

Alphabet Cards

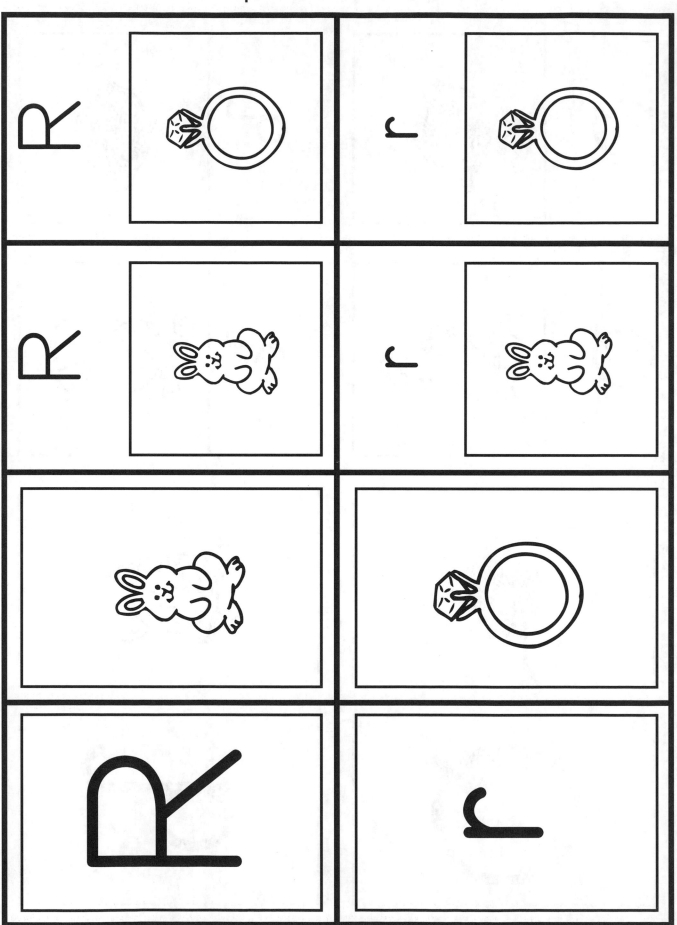

Alphabet Cards

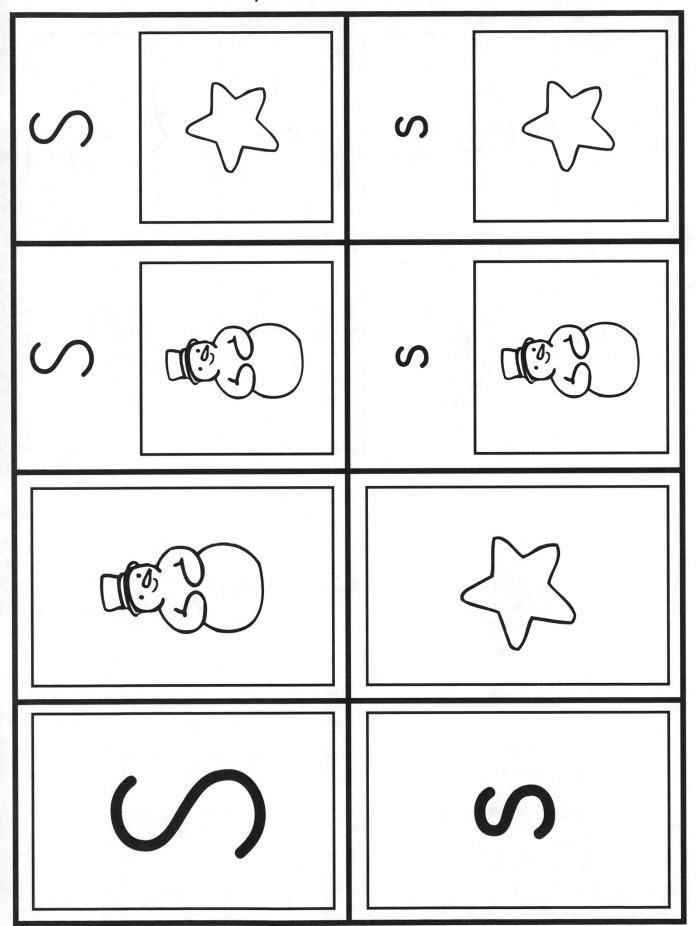

Alphabet Cards

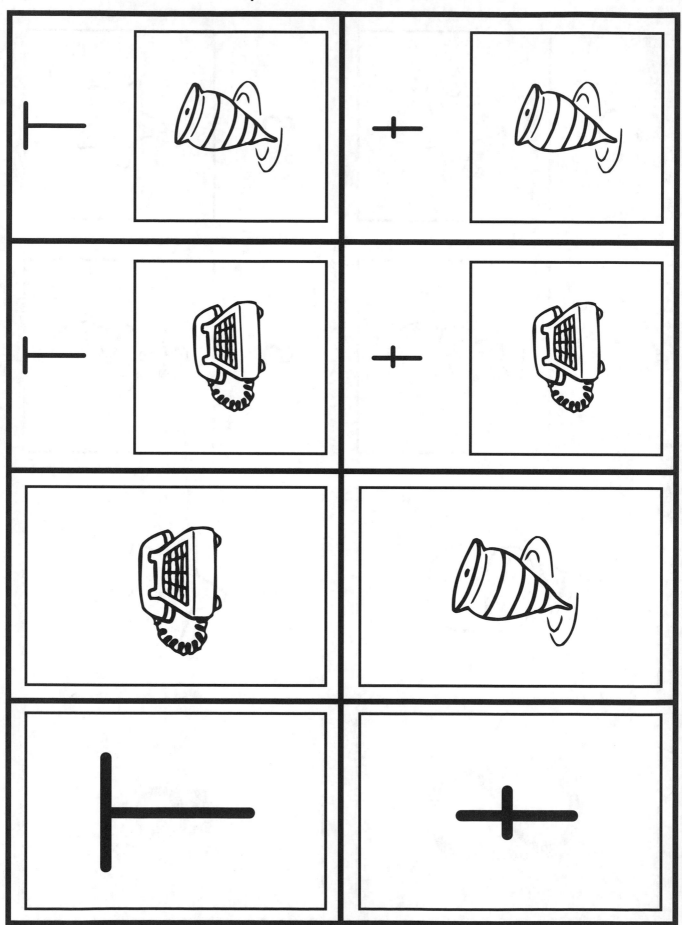

Alphabet Cards

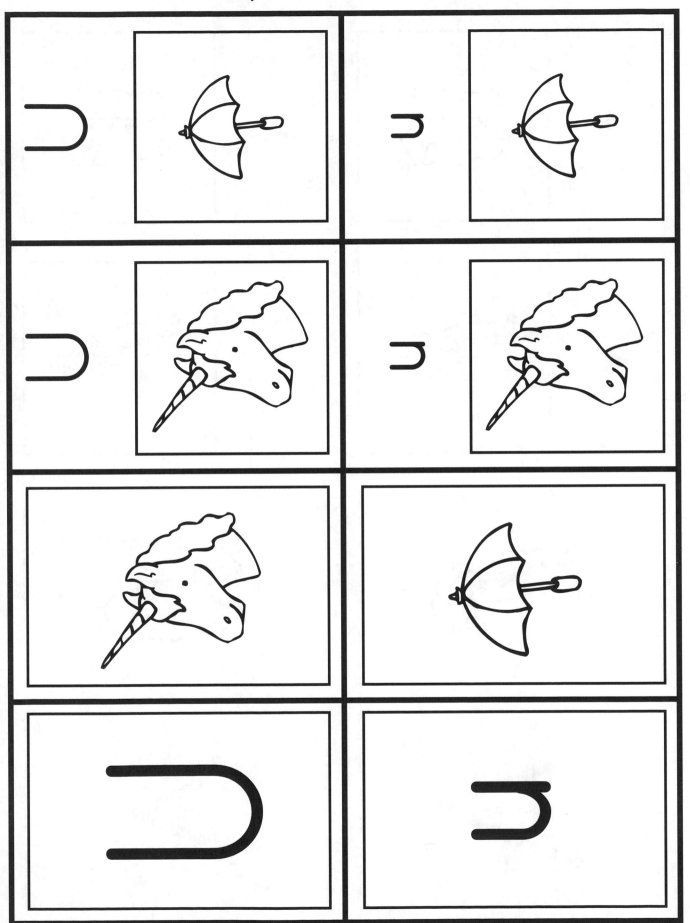

Alphabet Cards

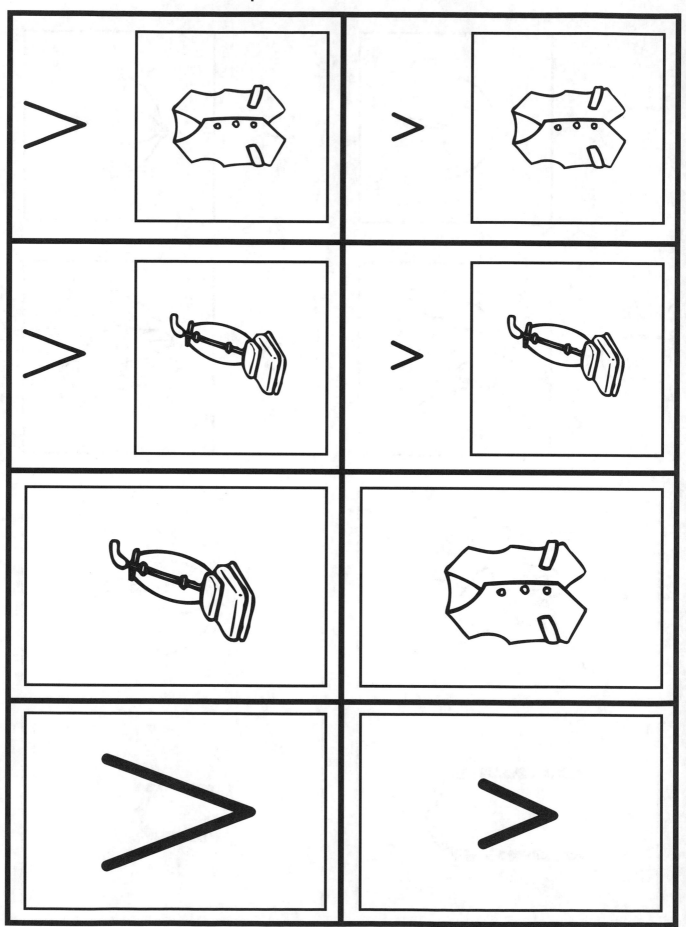

Alphabet Cards

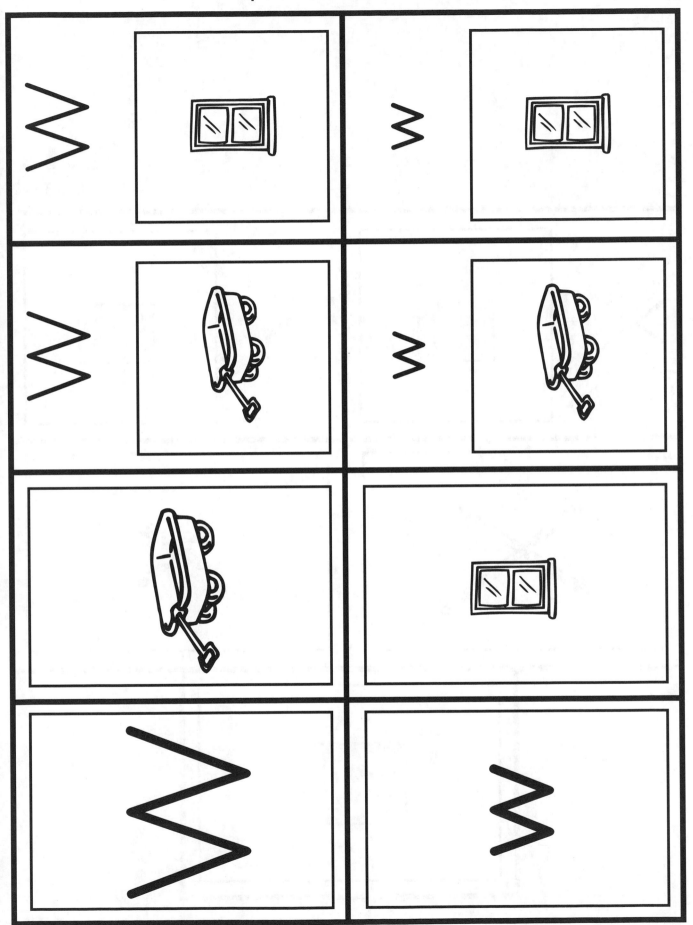

Alphabet Cards

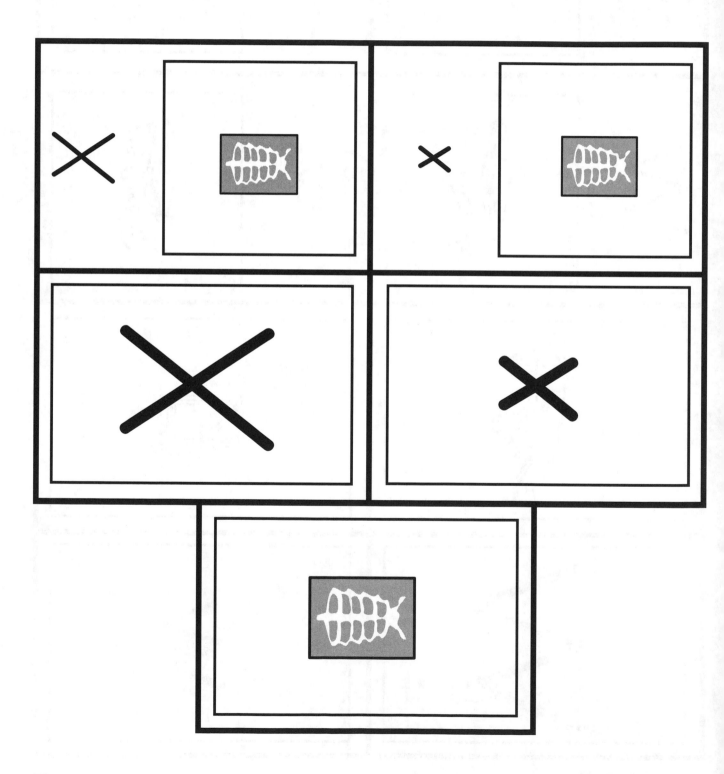

Alphabet Cards

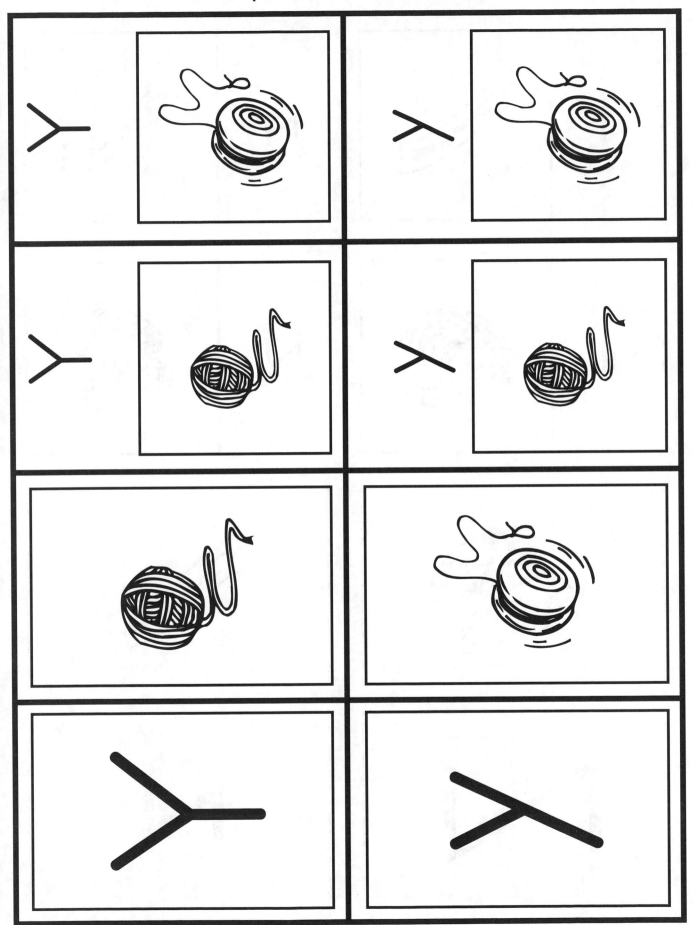

Alphabet Cards

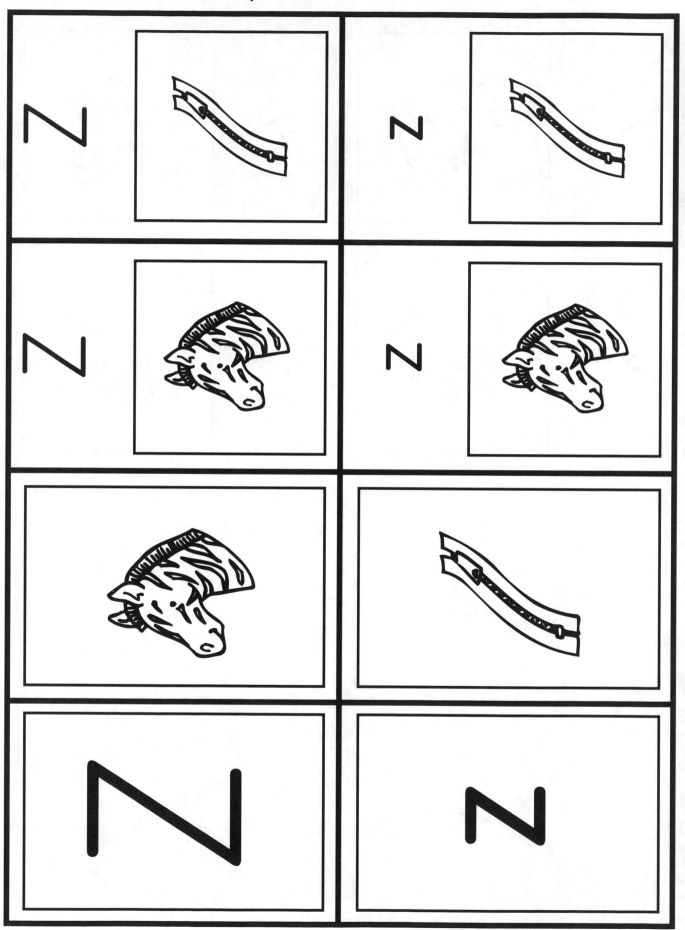

I Can Match the Alphabet Cards

I can match the alphabet on a bus.

I can match the alphabet on a bus.

I can match the alphabet on a car.

I can match the alphabet on a car.

I can match the alphabet on glasses.

I can match the alphabet on glasses.

I Can Match the Alphabet Cards

I can match the alphabet on a jar.

I can match the alphabet on a jar.

I Can Match the Alphabet Cards

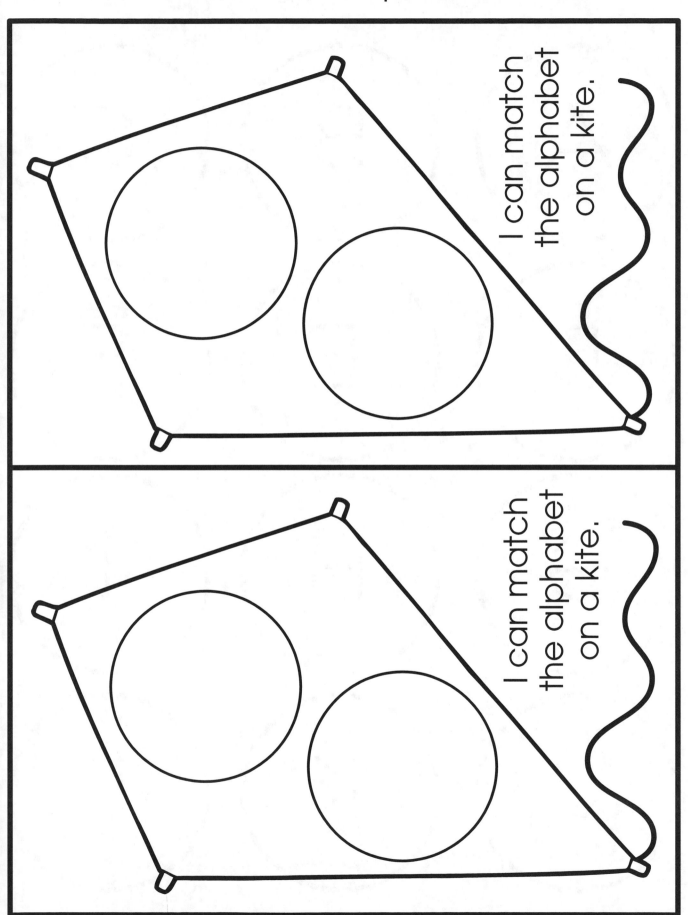

I can match the alphabet on a kite.

I can match the alphabet on a kite.

I Can Match the Alphabet Dots

I Can Match the Alphabet Dots

I Can Match the Alphabet Dots

I Can Match the Alphabet Dots

I Can Match the Alphabet Dots

I Can Match the Alphabet Dots

I Can Match the Alphabet Dots